Kitten Pairs

Each kitten has one that matches it. Draw a line between each kitten and its match.

On the Moon

Find and circle the **8** objects in this Hidden Pictures® puzzle.

What would you make with a giant cardboard box?

spatula

teacup

hairbrush

seashell

banana

wrench

fishhook

Ta-Da!

Circle at least **12** differences between these pictures.

Follow the Leader

Find and circle the **7** objects in this Hidden Pictures® puzzle.

slice of

toothbrush

Family Photo

Find and circle the **8** objects in this Hidden Pictures® puzzle.

What do the objects have in common?

book

ruler

door

envelope

harmonica

domino

chocolate bar

briefcase

7

Go, Team!

Circle each silly thing you see at this soccer game.

Can you think of 3 other types of sports?

Pattern Park

Circle each silly thing you see at this park. What patterns do you see?

Flying High

Follow the lines to see which kite belongs to which kid.

How do you think kites stay in the air?

Doggie Playdate

Follow each leash to see which dog belongs to which kid.

Point to the dog that's the longest.

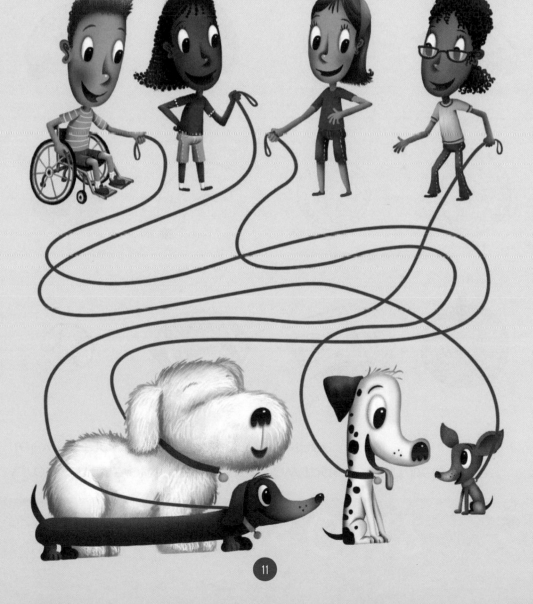

What Is Out?

Cross off the picture in each row that doesn't belong.
Tell why the other things go together.

What Is Different?

Cross off the picture in each row that is different.

Pizza Party

These pictures are all mixed up. Put them in order. Use **1**, **2**, and **3** to show the order.

Draw your favorite toppings on this pizza.

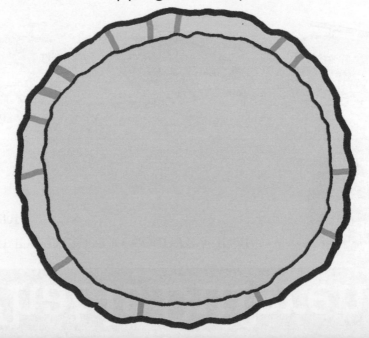

Flower Fun

These pictures are all mixed up. Put them in order. Use **1**, **2**, and **3** to show the order.

Color these vases. Then draw flowers to fill each vase.

Under the Sea

Each seahorse has one that matches it. Draw a line between each seahorse and its match.

Cake Match

Each cake has one that matches it. Draw a line between each cake and its match.

Can you think of 2 words that rhyme with *cake*?

Hit the Trail

Follow the path to help Amanda reach her friend Zack.

What are 2 reasons someone might ride a bike?

START

FINISH

Up the Hill

Follow the path to help the ant get out of the ant hill.

How many ants can you count?

FINISH

START

19

Painting Picnic

Circle at least **10** differences between these pictures.

What would you pack on a picnic?

New Shoes

Circle at least **12** differences between these pictures.

Goofy Garden

Circle each silly thing you see in this picture.

What would you plant in a garden?

Community Garden

Silly Ranch

Circle each silly thing you see in this picture.

Count Your Chickens

Follow this pattern to help the chick get to her mama.

What do you think this saying means: "Don't count your chickens before they hatch"?

What Is It?

Can you guess what this picture is?

Pair Them Up!

Draw a line from each sock to its match.

Cupcake Match

Draw a line from each cupcake to its match.

What a Ride!

Find and circle the **7** objects in this Hidden Pictures® puzzle.

zipper

ski

seashell

jug

bell

ladybug

It's a Strike!

Find and circle the **8** objects in this Hidden Pictures® puzzle.

What shapes do you see in this picture?

candle

pencil

pushpin

baseball

bowl

toothbrush

nail

slice of pizza

29

What Is Out?

Cross off the object in each group that doesn't belong with the others.

Who Is Out?

Cross off the animal in each row that doesn't belong with the others.

Plane Pairs

Draw a line from each plane to its match.

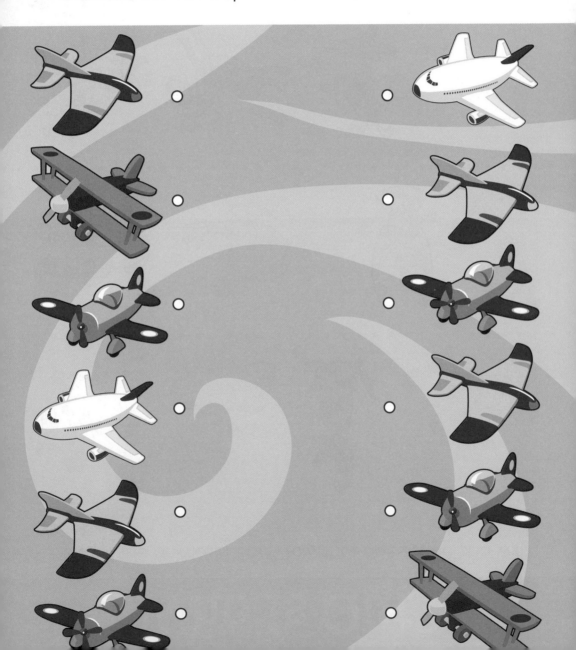

Dino Shapes

Color each rectangle ▮ blue. Color each square ▯ yellow. Color each circle ● green . Color each triangle ▲ red. What other shapes do you see?

Wiggle Pictures

These objects you might see in the sky have been twisted and turned. Can you figure out what each one is?

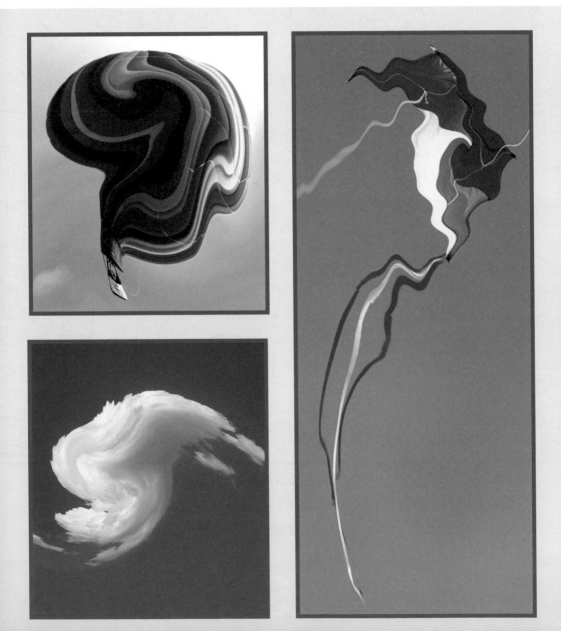

Wiggle Pictures

These yellow objects have been twisted and turned.
Can you figure out what each one is?

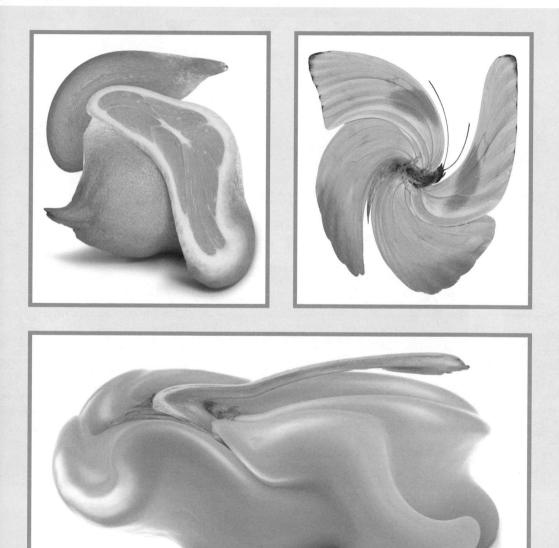

Space Travel

Follow this pattern to help Zeep get to his spaceship.

Finish the Patterns

What color comes next? Color the shape to complete the pattern in each row.

Summer Shopping

It's a busy day at the farmer's market. Draw a line to match each sign to the item for sale.

How much do the eggs cost? How much do the carrots cost?

Carrots

Flowers

Eggs

Jam

Whooo Matches?

Draw a line from each owl to its match.

Opposites

Night and *day* are opposites. Look at this picture and the one below. Which picture shows night? Which shows day? How can you tell?

Find and circle the 8 objects in this Hidden Pictures® puzzle.

horseshoe

star

slice of bread

feather

comb

glove

flashlight

Opposites

Hot and *cold* are opposites. Look at this picture and the one above. Which picture shows hot weather? Which shows cold weather? How can you tell?

Find and circle the 9 objects in this Hidden Pictures® puzzle.

drum

arrow

ruler

feather

fish

domino

spool of thread

artist's brush

frying pan

41

Matching Shapes

Draw a line from each shape on the left to the same shape on the right.

Say the name of each shape as you match it.

Matching Shapes

Draw a line from each shape on the left to the same shape on the right.

Say the name of each shape as you match it.

Spring in the Park

Circle at least **15** differences between this picture and the one below.

What do you like to do at a park? Why?

Silly Trail

Circle each silly thing you see.

Do you think a square bike tire would work? Why or why not?

Silly Bakery

Why do people put candles on birthday cakes?

Circle each silly thing you see.

47

Color Copy

Look at the fruits and vegetables on this page. Then color the fruits and vegetables below to match.

49

Dog Wash

Find and circle the **10** objects in this Hidden Pictures® puzzle.

pitcher

fish

flashlight

saltshaker

sock

light bulb

mitten

banana

carrot

Go Fish!

Find and circle the **7** objects in this Hidden Pictures® puzzle.

Why do you think the card game is called "Go Fish"?

heart

eraser

crescent moon

pencil

51

apple

bottle of glue

scissors

Whose Shoes?

Everyone's shoes got mixed up! Draw a line to connect each pair of shoes with the right person.

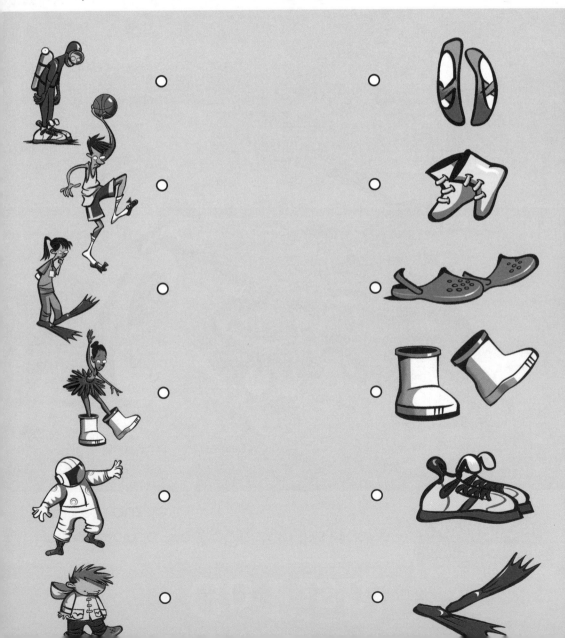

Who Goes Together?

Draw a line to connect each pair of things that go together.

Planting Seeds

These pictures are all mixed up. Put them in order to show how Jesse planted a garden. Use **1**, **2**, and **3** to show the order.

Draw a picture of what you'd like to grow in a garden.

Beach Day

These pictures are all mixed up. Put them in order to show Jasmine's day at the beach. Use **1**, **2**, and **3** to show the order.

What kind of sand castle would you like to make? Draw it below.

Building a Snowman

Use crayons or colored pencils to finish Sara and Seth's snowman.

Building Blocks

What are these kids building? Draw a picture of their block creation. Then find and circle the **6** objects in this Hidden Pictures® puzzle.

boot

envelope

bird

57

wedge of cheese

sailboat

fried egg

Doodle Art

What can you turn these squiggles into? A bird? A dragon? A snail? Draw what you think each squiggle can be.

Picture Day

What is this octopus taking a picture of? Draw it here. Then find and circle the **7** objects in this Hidden Pictures® puzzle.

pencil

canoe

cherry

lollipop

eyeglasses

ruler

spool of thread

This Is Me!

Say 3 things you like about yourself.

Draw a picture of yourself here.

Answers

Page 1
All Aboard!

Page 2
Here, Kitty!

Page 4
On the Moon

Page 5
Ta-Da!

Page 6
Follow the Leader

Page 7
Family Photo

Page 10
Flying High

Page 11
Doggie Playdate

Page 12
What Is Out?

Answers

Page 13
What Is Different?

Page 14
Pizza Party

2   1   3

Page 15
Flower Fun

2   3   1

Page 18
Hit the Trail

Page 19
Up the Hill

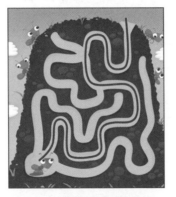

Page 20
Painting Picnic

Page 21
New Shoes

Page 24
Count Your Chickens

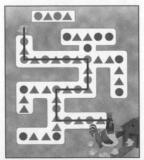

Page 25
What Is It?

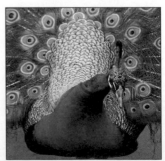

It's a peacock!

Answers

Page 28
What a Ride!

Page 29
It's a Strike!

Page 30
What Is Out?

Page 31
Who Is Out?

Page 34
Wiggle Pictures

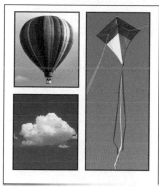

Page 35
Wiggle Pictures

Page 36
Space Travel

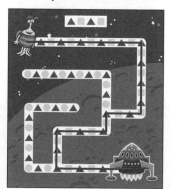

Page 37
Finish the Patterns

Page 38
Summer Shopping

Answers

Page 40
Opposites

Page 41
Opposites

Pages 44–45
Spring in the Park

Page 50
Dog Wash

Page 51
Go Fish!

Page 54
Planting Seeds

3   2   1

Page 55
Beach Day

3   1   2

Page 57
Building Blocks

Page 59
Picture Day